The Listening Game

HarperCollins *Children's Books*

It was a sunny day in Toyland.
Noddy had enjoyed spending the whole morning
delivering packages and had just finished the last
of his chores.

"Now I need to find another way to have fun,"
said Noddy, thoughtfully. "Maybe I can find
someone to play with!"

Meanwhile, the Goblins were arguing over a
fishing rod. "Give it to me, Sly!" Gobbo shouted
as he grabbed the fishing rod from Sly.
"Uh-oh," Sly replied when he caught sight
of Noddy. "Here's Noddy!"
"Act innocent!"
whispered Gobbo, as
he hid the fishing rod
behind his back.

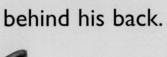

"Gobbo, are you going fishing?" Noddy asked. "Fishing is fun!"

"Fishing? Us?" spluttered Gobbo, hiding his fishing rod. "Not at all! Absolutely no fishing! Not us!"

"Well, maybe just a little fishing!" giggled Sly.

"Be quiet, you!" snapped Gobbo. "We're not going fishing at all!"

"Then why do you have a fishing rod?" Noddy asked.

"Fishing rod?" asked Gobbo. "Huh… what fishing rod?"

"The one behind your back, Gobbo!" chortled Sly.

"Mind your own beeswax!" shouted Gobbo. "I have more important things to do than answer silly questions. Goodbye!"

"Goblins can be so grumpy!" said Noddy, shaking his head.

Noddy went to see Mr Sparks at his garage.

"Hello, Mr Sparks," Noddy said, happily. "I have just finished all my deliveries! Would you like to play with me?"

"Sorry, Noddy. I can't right now," Mr Sparks replied. "I have a lot of things to fix. A bicycle, a cuckoo clock, and a bath tub drain. Busy, busy, busy!"

"OK, Mr Sparks," said Noddy. "I'll have to find someone else to play with."

Just then, Noddy spied Tessie Bear.

"Hello Tessie Bear!" Noddy said, excitedly.
"Would you like to play with me?"

"I can't quite play now, Noddy," replied Tessie Bear.
"I have to pull the weeds in my garden."

"Oh," said Noddy, sadly. "I will find someone
to play with. I will, I will, I will!"

Noddy went to visit Dinah Doll to see if she would play with him.

"Playing with you sounds like fun, Noddy," Dinah Doll said. "But I have to stay with my stall today."

"Not even for a little bit?" Noddy asked. "I'm sorry, Noddy," replied Dinah Doll. "But I've just started selling pails filled with sweets."

Suddenly, Dinah Doll
pointed to her stall.
She noticed that
one pail was missing.
   "That's strange,"
she said.
"There are only five
pails. I thought I had
six pails of candy!"

"Yes, that is
strange…"
sighed Noddy.
"Oh, there's no
one to play with!
Everyone has
a job to do!"

"I have an idea that might help!" said Dinah Doll.
"I'll teach you the Listening Game!"

"What is good about learning a new game if
there's no one to play it with?" asked Noddy, sadly.

"But the Listening Game you can play alone,"
explained Dinah Doll. "You close your eyes, listen,
and try to work out what is making the sounds
you hear."

Noddy closed his eyes and started to listen
to the sounds around him.

"Parp, parp!"

"I know that sound! It's my car!" cried Noddy.
"This might be fun after all! Thanks, Dinah Doll."

Happy now, Noddy skipped along Toy Town Street, listening all the time. Then he heard a squeaking noise.

"What could that be?" thought Noddy. "Could it be a mouse? Or maybe a rusty wheel?"

Just as it started getting louder, Noddy caught
sight of Mr Plod.

"It's Mr Plod!" cried Noddy. "With really
squeaky shoes!"

Noddy waved at Mr Plod. "This is fun," said
Noddy. "I want to play again!"

Noddy was so happy, he sang a song.

A sneeze,
A tap,
A woosh,
A snap!
It's fun to hear,
To lend an ear.
Listening!

A honk,
A squeak,
A laugh,
A shriek!
I figure out
What they're about.
Listening!

Next, Noddy headed over to Mr Sparks' garage
when he heard a loud clanging sound.

"That's an easy one!" Noddy cried. "I bet
Mr Sparks is fixing something in his garage."
Sure enough when Noddy turned the corner,
Mr Sparks was busy fixing his bicycle.

"I was right!" Noddy said, happily.

Then Noddy heard a tinkling bell sound.

"That's a hard one," thought Noddy. "I think…
I think… it might be Big-Ears on his bicycle!" Sure
enough, Big-Ears rode past on his shiny bicycle.

"Hello, Noddy!" Big-Ears cried.

"Hello, Big-Ears!" Noddy replied.

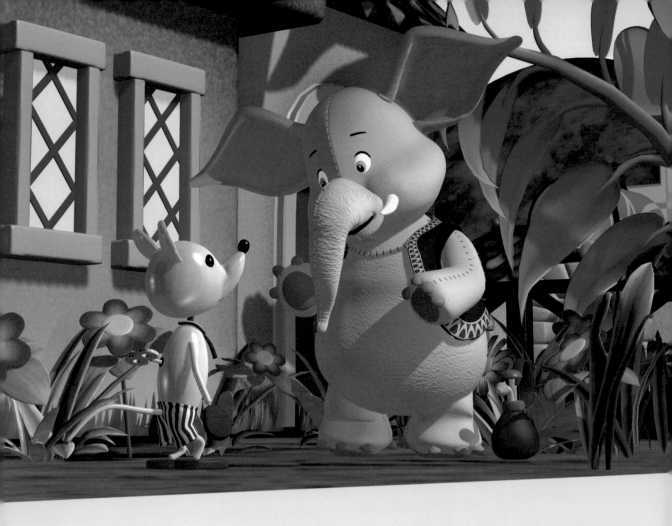

"I am going to play again!" said Noddy, as he closed
his eyes and began to listen.

Clockwork Mouse and Mr Jumbo were hiding
behind a tree, watching Noddy play his listening
game. They started giggling.

"That's Clockwork Mouse!" cried Noddy,
as they came out from behind the tree, laughing.

Then Martha Monkey decided to join in with Noddy's Listening Game. She crept up behind him and began to push his head.

"Let's see if he gets this one right," Martha Monkey said to herself.

"What is that noise?" Noddy asked as his head begain to nod. "I've heard that before. Hey, it's me!" Martha Monkey burst into a fit of giggles.

"Martha Monkey, stop making my head nod!"
Noddy cried.

"Hee-hee!" laughed Martha Monkey. "It's just
so much fun!"

"I love the Listening Game so much, even
Martha Monkey can't ruin it!' Noddy said, smiling.

And with that, Noddy headed back to Dinah Doll's
stall to thank her for teaching him the Listening Game.

When Noddy arrived, Mr Plod was inspecting the stall.

"Only two pails left," said Mr Plod, slowly. "Most confusing. Even I can't work it out and I'm a trained detective."

"It just doesn't make sense," Dinah Doll replied.

"What's happened?" asked Noddy, as he joined his friends.

"Hello, Noddy," said Dinah Doll, sadly. "More pails of candy have disappeared."

"They disappeared?" replied Noddy. "How?"

"I can't understand it! I turn away for one moment and when I turn back, another pail of candy is gone!" cried Dinah Doll.

"There is no one around who could have taken the pail," said Mr Plod. "I can't work it out!"

"I know!" said Noddy, suddenly. "Let's play the Listening Game!"

"This is no time for fun and games, Noddy," replied Mr Plod. "The case of the missing pails must be solved!"

"I really think it might help us save the case,"
pleaded Noddy.

"Very well, let's play this Listening Game
of yours," said Mr Plod.

With that, the friends began listening to the
sounds of Toy Town.

Suddenly, they heard a strange noise coming
from behind the stall.

"Listen," Noddy whispered. "Can you hear that sound?"

"Oh, this is so silly!" said Mr Plod.

"Maybe we should try and listen," Dinah Doll suggested.

They heard it again.

"I can't imagine what it could be!" Dinah Doll whispered.

"It's so familiar!" Noddy said. "I heard it right before the last pail disappeared."

The friends looked around to try and find where the noise was coming from.

"I've worked it out! It's a fishing rod!" Noddy cried, looking round. "I saw Sly and Gobbo with a fishing rod earlier today, too!"

Noddy looked up and, sure enough, the Goblins were hiding on the roof.

"Look, Mr Plod!" he cried, pointing at the naughty Goblins.

The Goblins had been using their fishing rod to steal Dinah Doll's pails!

Mr Plod was very angry. "Hey, you Goblins!" shouted Mr Plod. "Halt in the name of the Plod! You're under arrest for trespassing, stealing and... fishing without a licence!"

"Caught again," grumbled Sly, as he put down his fishing rod.

A little while later, Noddy was helping Dinah Doll at her stall.

"Thank you for helping me get my pails of candy, Noddy," said Dinah Doll, gratefully.

"Don't thank me, thank the Listening Game!" replied Noddy.

"I'm sorry, Noddy. What did you say?" replied Dinah Doll. "I wasn't listening!"

Noddy and Dinah Doll burst into fits of laughter and put all the pails safely back into Dinah Doll's stall.

First published in Great Britain by HarperCollins Children's Books in 2007
HarperCollins Children's Books is a division of HarperCollins Publishers Ltd,
77-85 Fulham Palace Road, Hammersmith, London W6 8JB

1 3 5 7 9 10 8 6 4 2

ISBN-13: 978-0-00-722354-1
ISBN-10: 0-00-722354-4

Printed and bound by
Printing Express Ltd, Hong Kong

NODDY™

Star in your very own PERSONALISED Noddy book!

In just 3 easy steps your child can join Noddy in a Toyland adventure!

1 Go to www.MyNoddyBook.co.uk

2 Personalise your book

3 Checkout!

3 Great Noddy adventures to choose from:

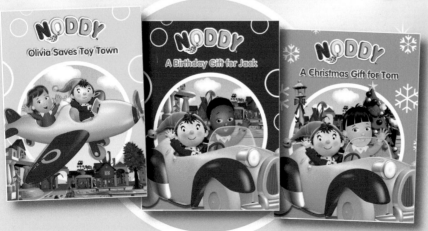

'Your child' Saves Toytown
Soar through a rainbow in Noddy's aeroplane to help him save Toytown.

A Gift for 'your child'
Noddy composes a song for your child in this story for a special occasion.

A Christmas Gift for 'your child'
Noddy composes a song for your child in a Christmas version of the above story.

Visit today to find out more and create your personalised Noddy book!

www.MyNODDYBook.co.uk